My Cousin Lili

Written by
Amy Lightfoot
with **Sally Lightfoot**

Illustrated by
Teofilo Padilla

MyCousinLili.com

ISBN 978-0-692-88040-1

Published by LiliArte
Written by Amy Lightfoot with Sally Lightfoot
Illustrated by Teofilo Padilla
Cover Design & Layout by Janie Owen-Bugh
Edited by Julie Denker

This book is dedicated with love to
my cousin, Lili, and all children with
special needs around the world.
~ Amy Lightfoot

My name is Amy.
I live in the United States.

Lili lives far, far
away in another
country called
Honduras.

I still remember how I met my cousin Lili. My aunt moved to Honduras when I was very little.

She found Lili in a hospital. Lili needed someone to take care of her.

So, my aunt became her new mom.

That Christmas, my aunt and Lili flew on a big plane to visit my family.

We all met her at the airport. I was so excited to see my new cousin!

I wanted to play and sing and run and jump and talk with Lili ...

but, I quickly realized she wasn't like me.

She didn't know how to talk. She had just learned how to walk.

She didn't know how to play with any of my toys.

I don't know what to do.

I didn't quite know what to do.

So, I just did what Lili did.

First, we twirled and twirled all around.

We were explorers!

Then, we hummed and hummed with our voices going high and low.

We were a beautiful choir!

After that, we found all kinds of things to flap and flap, up and down.

We were treasure hunters!

I thought it was amazing that even though Lili didn't say any words, we could talk and talk for hours with our smiles and giggles.

We were
best friends.

I've learned so much from Lili.

Lili couldn't talk.

I learned that just because someone can't talk doesn't mean they don't have anything to say.

Lili loved little things.

I learned that the littlest of things
can make you happy.

Lili would sometimes look right at me.

I learned that people can show love with just their eyes.

Lili didn't sit still very often.

I learned that you have to get up and twirl to see the world.

Lili wasn't like me. She was very, very special.

I learned to love everyone …
even if they are different.

I love my cousin Lili...
she changed my life forever!

"Let all that you do be done in love."
~ 1 Corinthians 16:14 NASB

CPSIA information can be obtained
at www.ICGtesting.com
Printed in the USA
LVIC04n1947030617
536551LV00001B/1

* 9 7 8 0 6 9 2 8 8 0 4 0 1 *